Liverpool
Cartoons by Bill Stott

CW00383114

Liverpool is the funniest place I've ever been. Liverpool humour is dead pan and deadly. It can demolish pretentious people and rip the glitter off posers. After twenty-seven years of living in and near Liverpool I've dared to do a cartoon book about the place. I bet some of the things said about the book are funnier than what's in it.

Bill Stott

Origination by: Ian Boumphrey - Desk Top Publisher

Published by: Ian & Marilyn Boumphrey
                 "The Nook" Acrefield Road Prenton Wirral L42 8LD
Printed by: Arroweline Hoylake L47 2BS

ISBN   1-899241-02-7

Price
£2.99

"It fell off the back of a lorry . . ."

" SCOUSERS ARE OPEN & FRIENDLY ~ ALWAYS READY TO DIRECT STRANGERS • • • • • • "

"Yer go down 'ere - past de er, wossname, den straight on round de, y'know, den look for a wossname on yer right . . . "

"*The new management haven't got the speed right . . .*"

"Go and get your Grandad before he starts one of his
'I remember when I was a lad' sessions."

"OK - it's a Mark II - remember - all we need are windscreen wipers &
the passenger door."

"Yer gorrenny nudes in dere?"

"Hey Darlene! Guess what - these two guys went to school with John Lennon AND for only £50 they're prepared to take us on a tour of pubs he used to frequent!"

"Liverpool Anglican Cathedral begun 1904, finished 1978.
Must have been a Council job."

"Hang on - this could be interesting . . ."

"Good afternoon officer - I was hurrying back to my vehicle from the hossie where my Gran is gravely ill, when I inadvertently knocked over this Traffic Warden . ."

"Ey, pal, lend us three hundred quid for a bath & a shave, a new suit, a fashionable haircut and a portable phone - so's I can get back into Yates's"

"Our Darren's just spotted a bus less than 12 years old!"

"Western Approaches Secret Operations Room? Dead secret mate - but give us a quid & I'll tell you."

"There you are pal - the beak's a bit bent - it fell off the top of a tall building."

"Two pints of Chablis and a Chardonnay over Muscadet, pal . . ."

"She does the announcements at Lime Street Station."

"And the defence will prove that far from breaking & entering, the accused, as an ex-employee, was merely trying to help his old firm by highlighting security weaknesses."

"Show biz? Our Billy? Nearest he ever got to that was being run over by the taxi Gerry Marsden had just got out of."

"Dog still not turned up then?"

"'Course it's not new - look at the label - 1992!"

"You'd like to see some football trophies but you're pushed for time? Go see Everton's - that won't take long."

"Oops! Sorry . . ."

"I'm sorry, but we already have window cleaning
arrangements in place."

*"Captain's compliments ladies . . . Would you mind
sitting more towards the middle?"*

Dear Mrs Bradshaw,
Please can you let Tracy out from school at 3·00pm as she has to go to the opticians with her eyes and they close at 3·30.
Yours Truly
D. Murphy (Mrs)

"OK - here comes another - and this time I get the funny hat, you get the shirt & kecks."

"I wonder who's first? - I didn't know there was a league . . ."

"You're just too damned soft on these street traders, Murphy."

"Get down 'ere, our Terry!"

"I know we mustn't sell anything new - that's why our kid's havin' a quick drag on every ciggie."

"Him? He was a Liverpool Taxi Driver . . ."

"He's from London officer. He suggested that scousers were aggressive & unsophisticated, so, 'e gorra smack."

"There goes Lady Muck - got all the questions right on 'Hold your plums' on Sunday – they wont ask HER again!"

"Is it a show dog? Too right! Show this down the ale 'ouse & you'll never be burgled!"

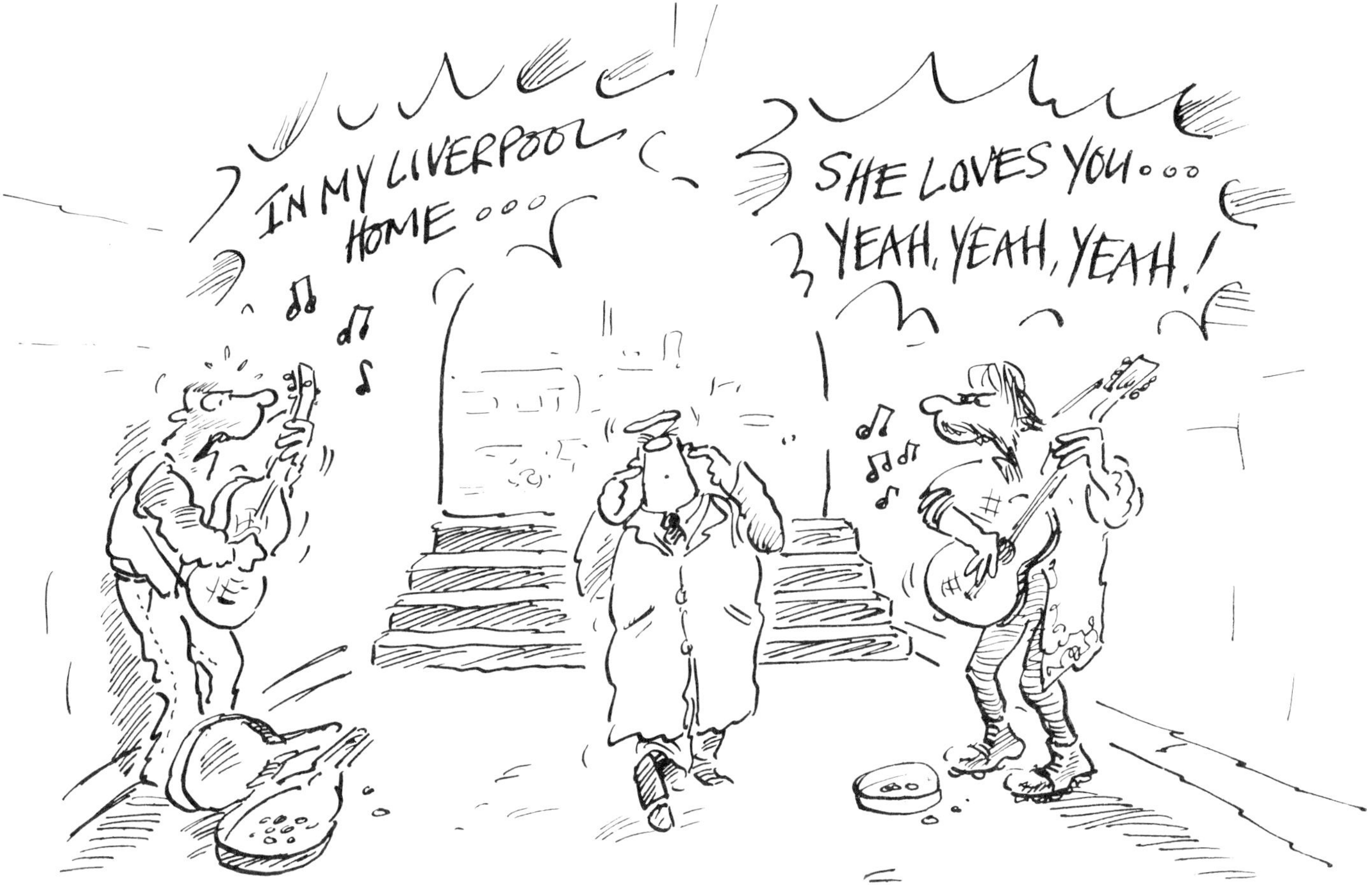
IN MY LIVERPOOL HOME...
SHE LOVES YOU... YEAH, YEAH, YEAH!

"*I asked them for a grant to get yer Dad tarted up - but I've heard nothin'.*"

OLD SCOUSE JOKES
NO1 IN A SERIES OF 579
HOW DO YOU SELL A PIG TO A DEAF BLOKE?
I DON'T KNOW. HOW DO YOU SELL A PIG TO A DEAF BLOKE?
D'YER WANNA BUY A PIG?

"You don't want to go in there mate - most of the furniture's nicked and HE'S from Ormskirk."

"Don't be scared, our Gary, your Gran hasn't been here for 30 years, so she thought she'd dress the part."

"How many times do I have to tell you, our Lee -
You don't do that in new trainers!"